Gone but Not Forgotten

By Dennis P. Eichhorn. Artwork by Pat Moriarity.

Ah, the early '80s...

...Seattle was really cookin' then!

GO SONICS

AURORA

I was working for the Seattle Sun, a liberal weekly. The job had its moments...

Denny, can you cover the Plasmatics at the Showbox Theater tonight?

You bet!

GOSONICS!

THE HEATS AT ASTOR PARK

TAP TAP

The Showbox was packed, and the Plasmatics were outrageous!

W.O.W.!

4

VIAGRA FALLS

14

15

16

ONCE I ALMOST GOT CAUGHT. I WAS SMOKING A JOINT IN MY BACK BEDROOM ONE NIGHT WITH THE WINDOW OPEN, WHEN I HEARD A NOISE OUTSIDE...

SOMETIMES I WONDER WHAT WE'RE DOING, SONNY... DON'T WORRY ABOUT IT, RICARDO!

MIAMI VICE

RUSTLE SNAP!

OO WHAT' TH' FUCK WAS THAT!

I WENT OUTSIDE AND CHECKED, BUT THERE WASN'T ANYONE TO BE SEEN

I COULD HAVE SWORN I HEARD SOMETHING!

STILL, I WAS PARANOID, SO I CLEANED UP THE PLACE. AND IT WAS A GOOD THING I DID, BECAUSE THE NEXT DAY...

KNOCK KNOCK!

HUH? UH...JUST A MINUTE!!

IT WAS MY LANDLORD, ACCOMPANIED BY A GRIM-FACED STRANGER.

WHAT'S THIS ALL ABOUT?

AH, GOOD MORNING, MR. EICHHORN! MISTER SMITH HERE IS INTERESTED IN BUYING THIS BUILDING AND HE'D LIKE TO TAKE A QUICK LOOK AROUND... YOU DON'T MIND, DO YOU?

UH... I GUESS NOT... C'MON IN.

The STORY of MINESHAFT

"MINESHAFT" was born in a 15 x 15 foot cabin in Vermont.

It was named after a bar in La Paz.

DNA can be traced to Irving Stettner's STROKER, a small magazine that operated on a shoestring.

A writer and watercolorist, Irving published Henry Miller, Paul Bowles, Tommy Trantino, Albert Cossery and others from 1974 until he died in 2004.

Stettner befriended and contributed to MINESHAFT with advice, art and writing.

Stettner cover art on issue one

MINESHAFT

He also provided his detailed step by step guide to putting a magazine together by hand.

Irving introduced MINESHAFT to many poets. Several were published in the early issues.

One evening, Everett and Gioia, MINESHAFT's founders, rented the movie "Crumb".

Ev later wrote him a letter, inviting him to contribute.

A few months later:

Look! A letter from R. Crumb!

photocopies of eighteen sketchbook drawings

Eventually, MINESHAFT began to feature work by underground comics artists like Robert Armstrong, B.N. Duncan, Mary Fleener, Jay Lynch, Aline Kominsky Crumb, Frank Stack and Kim Deitch.

MINESHAFT is more than just a comic book or small magazine. It's an organism! and it continues to grow.

ONE OF THE "YOUNGER" CONTRIBUTORS

PAT MORIA-RITY

END

WWW.MINESHAFTMAGAZINE.COM

THE HATE MAN COMETH

Story by
DENNIS P. EICHHORN

Artwork by
TOM VAN DEUSEN

It was a sparkling Spring day in Berkeley, when I met up with cartoonist B.N. Duncan...

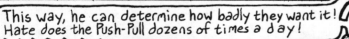

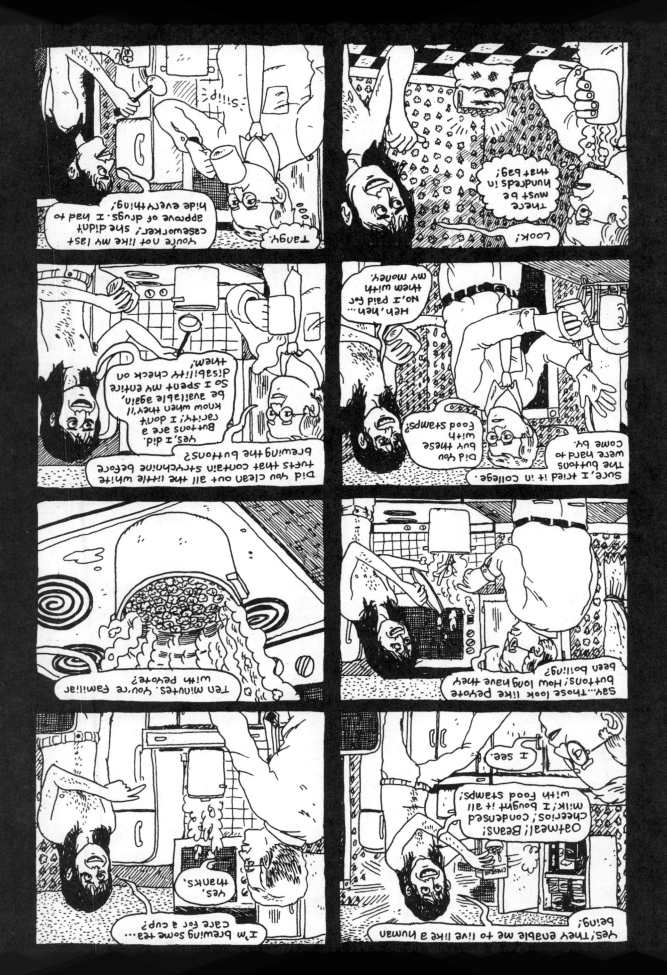

OUR "NAVAL BASE KITSAP" IS HOME TO TWO NIMITZ-CLASS NUCLEAR-POWERED SUPER CARRIERS – ARMED WITH MISSILES AND CARRYING 90 AIRCRAFT APIECE – AND TWO SEAWOLF-CLASS SUBMARINES!

THIS IS WHERE ALL THE NAVY'S NUCLEAR-POWERED SHIPS AND SUBS ARE EVENTUALLY DISMANTLED... EVEN THE REACTORS!

THERE'S A FLEET OF MOTHBALLED SHIPS STANDING BY IN SINCLAIR INLET, INCLUDING FOUR AIRCRAFT CARRIERS!

AN UNDERSEA WARFARE SCHOOL, WHERE BOTH HUMANS AND DOLPHINS ARE TRAINED IN AQUA-COMBAT, IS A FEW MILES AWAY!

ELEVEN NUCLEAR-POWERED SUBMARINES ARE BASED AT NEARBY BANGOR, AND A CONTINGENT OF MARINES GUARDS THE 2,364 NUCLEAR WARHEADS!

BAN THE BOMB!

DIS... NOW

AIN'T NOBODY MESSIN' WITH OUR NUKES!

GIT ON OUTTA HERE, PEACENIKS!

...NOT WEAPONRY

NO MI...

NO WA...

DESTR... LEFT THE RIGHT NWO

THE NAVY'S LARGEST FUEL DEPOT IS THERE, TOO!

IF THE USA IS EVER ATTACKED, KITSAPALACHIA (BREMERTON AND ITS ENVIRONS) IS SURELY A MAJOR TARGET IN SOMEBODY'S WARGAME!

WE'LL STRIKE FIRST, AND DESTROY A FOURTH OF THE GREAT SATAN'S NUCLEAR ARSENAL!

JUST ABOUT EVERYBODY IN KITSAPALACHIA SEEMS TO HAVE A CONNECTION TO THE NAVY OR MARINE CORPS!

I WAS BORN IN THE NAVAL HOSPITAL!

I SPENT TWENTY YEARS IN THE NAVY, AND FIVE IN THE SHIPYARD!

I MET MY HUSBAND IN MANILA!

YEAH, AND WE STAYED HERE AFTER I WAS DISCHARGED.

SOME OF THE VETERANS HEREABOUTS ARE MEAN AND DEADLY, TRAINED BY UNCLE SAM TO KILL IN A VARIETY OF WAYS.

IT ISN'T A GOOD IDEA TO GO OUT LOOKING FOR TROUBLE IN THE LOCAL BARS...

BECAUSE YOU MIGHT RUN INTO SOMEONE WHO'S ARMED AND DANGEROUS...

...LIKE CHRISTIAN!

WE MET AFTER I'D BEEN DRIVING A CAB FOR SEVERAL MONTHS. HIS REPUTATION PRECEEDED HIM.

I JUST DROPPED OFF THE CRAZIEST BASTARD EVER!

WHO'S THAT?

HIS NAME'S "CHRISTIAN"!

CHRISTIAN WAS AN EX-SEAL WHO'D BECOME A HEAVY-EQUIPMENT OPERATOR WHEN HE WASN'T WORKING, HE WAS DRINKING, TAKING DRUGS...

YOU FUCKING CUNT!

DON'T HIT ME AGAIN!

WAAAHHH!

...OR BEATING UP HIS WIFE!

Panel 1:
AFTER A JUDGE JERKED CHRISTIAN'S DRIVER'S LICENSE...

THAT'S ONE D.U.I. TOO MANY!

Panel 2:
...HE GOT AROUND TOWN IN TAXICABS!

PLEASE SEND A CAB TO BROOKSIDE PARK, UNIT 5-F.

WAAH!!

Panel 3:
CHRISTIAN'S MODUS OPERANDI WAS TO GO TO A BAR AND RAISE HELL UNTIL THEY THREW HIM OUT!

NOBODY TALKS TO ME LIKE THAT!

BUT I DIDN'T SAY ANYTHING!

THAT'S IT... PACK UP AND LEAVE, FELLA!

SOMETIMES THEY'D CALL THE COPS... BUT USUALLY THEY'D JUST PHONE FOR A CAB.

Panel 4:
CHRISTIAN SOON ALIENATED ALL THE LOCAL CAB DRIVERS.

DIG IT, MAN... MY K-BAR AND GLOCK... I'M READY TO ROCK!

Panel 5:
BEFORE LONG NOBODY WOULD PICK HIM UP!

HEH! BROKE TWO KNUCKLES ON THAT TURKEY!

DON'T BLEED ALL OVER THE SEAT!

Panel 6:
NOBODY BUT ME, THAT IS.

NUMBER FIVE, PICK UP CHRISTIAN AT HOME.

TEN-FOUR.

CHRISTIAN WAS AN ASSHOLE, BUT HE TIPPED WELL.

19

LET'S GO, BEFORE I LOSE CONTROL AND WASTE THESE CLOWNS.

WE LEFT, AS EVERYONE AVERTED THEIR EYES...

DON'T MOVE PUSSIES... I WANT TO CARRY THIS TABLEAU IN MY MIND FOREVER!

...ANXIOUS FOR CHRISTIAN TO DEPART, SO THEY COULD GET BACK TO BEING TOUGH CUSTOMERS.

WHERE TO?

HOME, JEROME...

I'M FEELING KIND OF HORNY.

SNORK!

SNORK!

AHHHH...WANT A BLAST?

NO THANKS... I'M THE DESIGNATED DRIVER.

WE DROVE ACROSS TOWN, AND WERE STOPPED AT A LIGHT, WHEN...

HEY BUTT-FACE! WHAT THE FUCK ARE YOU LOOKIN' AT?

TAXI!

CROWN 111339 HOW'S MY DRIVE 555?

PO'BOY G 3 NRA

THE LIGHT CHANGED, AND WE WERE OFF!

WHAT DID YOU SAY, DICK-HEAD?

I'LL COME OVER AND SHOW YOU!

I ASKED WHAT YOU'RE LOOKIN' AT, SHIT-FOR-BRAINS!

BACK OFF, MOTHER-FUCKER!

CHRISTIAN! STOP!

HEY... I'M NOT DONE WITH YOU!

WHOOSH!

HONK!

RATES AIRPORT

YOU SHOULD'VE LET ME JUMP! I COULD'VE MADE IT!

YOU'RE A MENACE!!

I COULD'VE KILLED THAT MOUTHY SON OF A BITCH WITH JUST THESE TWO FINGERS.

HELL... I COULD KILL YOU IF I FELT LIKE IT! JUST ONE QUICK JAB THROUGH THE EYE... AND YOU'RE DEAD MEAT.

THAT DID IT!

SO WHAT'S STOPPING YOU? GO AHEAD! I'VE HAD IT! YOU'LL BE DOING ME A FAVOR!

AT THE TIME, I MEANT IT!

JUST TAKE ME HOME. IF I KILLED YOU, THE TAXI WOULD CRASH.

EIGHT-FIFTY.

KEEP THE CHANGE.

SEE YA NEXT TIME!

YEAH RIGHT.

TAXI

RATES

THE NEXT TIME NEVER CAME, BECAUSE LATER THAT DAY....

THAT'S IT... I QUIT!

WHY'S THAT, NUMBER FIVE?

IT'S THE **CHRISTIAN** THING TO DO!

CLUNK!

11-06-13

ALL SECURE

TEN-FOUR!

WHAT'S GOING ON?

SHHH! BE QUIET!

WE WERE JUST TAKING A HIKE.. WE DIDN'T EXPECT TO FIND.... SHIT IN THE WOODS

BY DENNIS P. EICHHORN · ARTWORK · PAUL OLLSWANG ©JUNE 95

MY FRIEND EVE & I WERE CABIN SITTING FOR SOME FRIENDS IN THE CASCADES, NEAR MOUNT RAINIER~

THIS IS GREAT!!! NO PHONE-CALLS!! AND NO PEOPLE!

AND IT'S ALL OURS, 'TIL WEDNESDAY!

WE UNPACKED - AND DECIDED TO EXPLORE THE COUNTRYSIDE~

READY.

LET'S GO!

AN HOUR LATER ~ & TWO MILES AWAY

LOOK! THERE'S A MAN WITH A GUN!!

QUICK! DUCK OUT OF SIGHT

WHAT'S THE MATTER?

NUMBER TWO: REPORT

IT ISN'T HUNTING SEASON!!

ALL'S SECURE

I WONDER WHAT HE'S UP TO ..
LET'S FOLLOW HIM AND FIND OUT..
AFTER SEVERAL MINUTES OF CAREFULLY CREEPING THRU THE UNDERBRUSH
LOOK AT THAT!
WHAT ON EARTH ?
NOW, THAT'S A STRANGE LITTLE SET-UP
EVERY-THING COOL?
NO PROBLEMS, -SO FAR---

WE STAYED HIDDEN FOR SEVERAL HOURS — IN THE LATE AFTERNOON — THE TWO SENTRIES HAD A TARGET-PRACTICE SESSION

KAPOW

THOSE GUN-SHOTS ARE MAKING ME NERVOUS —

LET'S GET OUT OF HERE!

KAPOW

THERE'S NO TELLING WHAT THOSE CHARACTERS ARE COOKING UP IN THAT TRAILER!

THAT'S FOR SURE!

BACK AT THE CABIN — WE CLEANED UP AND PREPARED DINNER —

I WONDER WHAT THE FUCK THOSE GUYS ARE INTO?

METHEDRINE, CRACK, EXPLOSIVES — IT COULD BE ANYTHING

I THINK WE OUGHT TO GIVE THEM A WIDE BERTH

GOOD IDEA

WE STAYED AWAY FROM OUR MYSTERIOUS NEIGHBORS — AND — THREE DAYS LATER OUR FRIENDS RETURNED

THERE'S NO PLACE LIKE HOME!

WELCOME BACK!

NATURALLY~~ WE TOLD THEM ABOUT WHAT WE'D SEEN~~

"AND THERE WERE TWO GUYS WEARING CAMOUFLAGED CLOTHING, USING WALKIE-TALKIES~ AND FIRING RIFLES~ AND ANOTHER GUY, MESSING AROUND WITH SOME LAB EQUIPMENT INSIDE A TRAILER~"

AND~ IT LOOKS LIKE THEY'RE OPERATING A PROPANE-POWERED GENERATOR~ THEY'VE GOT A BACK-HOE, TOO~

HMMMM

WE SAW THOSE PEOPLE DRIVING IN LAST WEEK~ THEY MADE TWO TRIPS~ ONE TO HAUL THE BACKHOE, AND ANOTHER FOR THE TRAILER~

~WE THOUGHT THEY WORKED FOR WEYERHAUSER~ THEY OWN ALL THE LAND OVER THAT WAY.

THOSE GUYS ARE TRESS-PASSERS!!!!

ARE YOU GOING TO CALL THE LAW?

NO.

~I'VE GOT A FEW PLANTS GROWING OVER IN THAT NECK OF THE WOODS~ ~AND I DON'T WANT THE COPS TO STUMBLE ACROSS 'EM~

LET'S JUST LEAVE THOSE GUYS ALONE

WE'LL GET ANOTHER LOOK AT THEM, EVENTUALLY~ THAT'S THE ONLY ROAD, IN OR OUT

VROOM VRRROOM VRP

WHAT'S THAT NOISE, DENNY?

SOUNDS LIKE A BACKHOE, WAY OFF IN THE DISTANCE

RRRRRRRRRRRRRRRR

HERE THEY COME!

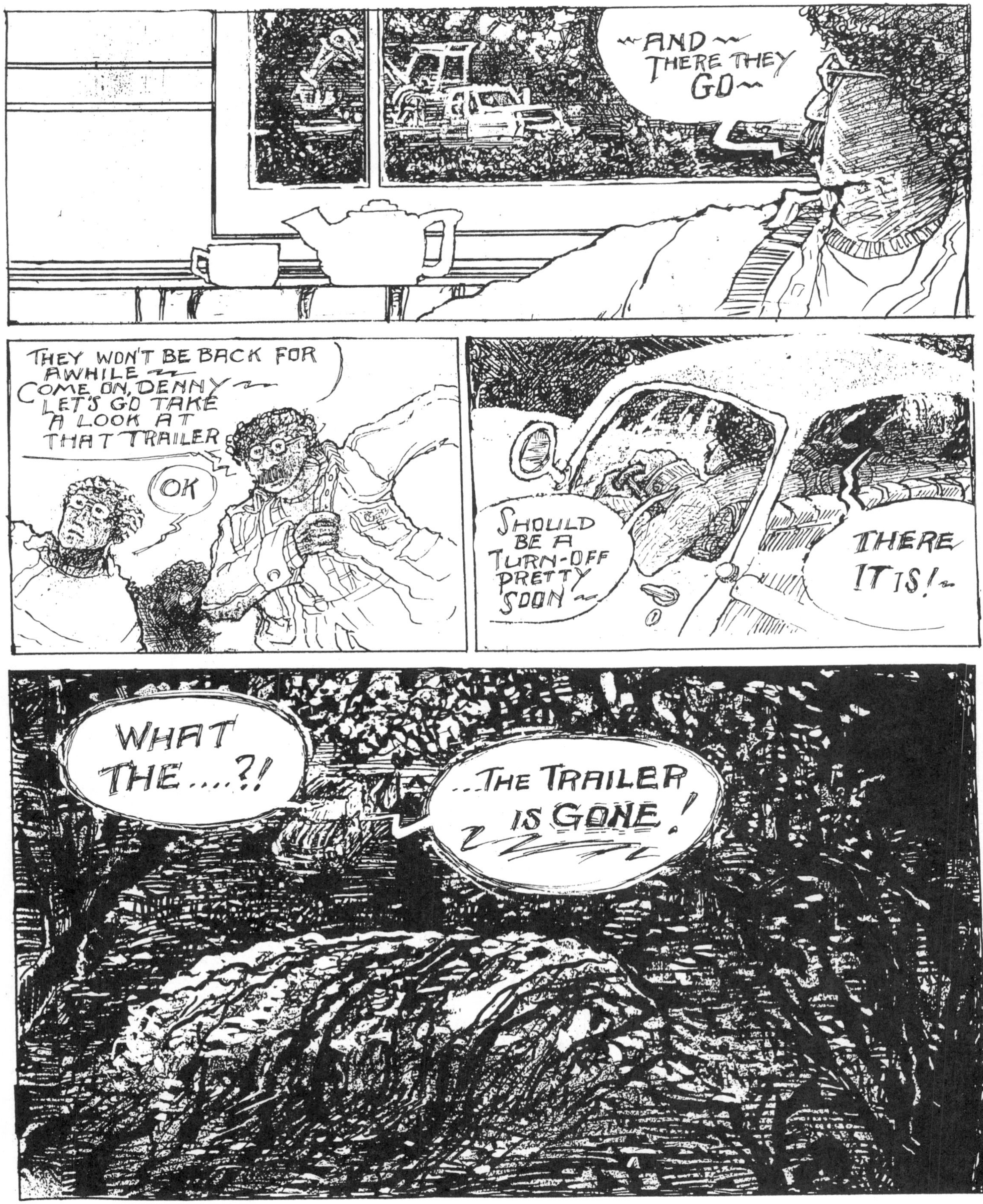

~AND~ THERE THEY GO~

THEY WON'T BE BACK FOR AWHILE~ COME ON, DENNY~ LET'S GO TAKE A LOOK AT THAT TRAILER

OK

SHOULD BE A TURN-OFF PRETTY SOON~

THERE IT IS!~

WHAT THE....?!

...THE TRAILER IS GONE!

JESSE LIVES! (sort of)!

BY DENNIS P. EICHHORN
ART BY SEAN M. HURLEY ©2003

The difference between me and other poets is I am really a spider...

If you dare condemn my life, it will come after you with a sharpened rake!

These men look confused like fish getting clubbed on the pier...

Get that fucker on the wall and *tear him loose*...

LET'S GET ONE THING STRAIGHT: I WASN'T A CLOSE PERSONAL FRIEND OF THE LATE JESSE BERNSTEIN. SURE, I'D SEEN AND HEARD HIS HIGH-OCTANE PERFORMANCES AT NUMEROUS SEATTLE VENUES...

Wow!

I just loved your performance!

Me too!

I'D SEEN HIM AROUND BELLTOWN—

--AND WE'D EXCHANGED PLEASANTRIES AT A COUPLE OF PARTIES—

Wanna go to a superbowl party?

You're kidding, right?

— BUT THAT WAS ABOUT IT. STILL, WHEN NEWS OF HIS SUICIDE ON OCTOBER 21, 1991 CIRCULATED—

⸢Sob⸣ They found his body in a cabin on Cape Flattery! ⸢choke⸣ There's a memorial at the Cyclops tonight.

No shit? I'll see you there.

IT CAME AS A REAL SHOCK!

SCUD (SUBTERRANEAN COOPERATIVE OF URBAN DREAMERS) WAS AN ART COLLECTIVE WHERE SOME OF JESSE'S CLOSEST FRIENDS LIVED. HE'D BEEN A FAMILIAR FIGURE THERE AND AT THE CYCLOPS, A CAFE IN THE SAME BUILDING. HUNDREDS OF PEOPLE GATHERED.

Everybody's wearing black. As usual.

CYCLOPS

He was 40 years old!

How could he stab himself in the neck *three times?*

CANDLES WERE LIT, AND MOURNERS CONVERSED IN LOW TONES. NO ONE TOOK CHARGE, AS BEFIT AN IMPROMPTU POST-BEAT MEMORIAL.

REMARKABLY, JESSE'S UNTIMELY DEATH BREATHED NEW LIFE INTO HIS WORK. HIS FAME SPREAD AROUND THE WORLD, AS HE CAME TO BE REGARDED AS "THE GODFATHER OF GRUNGE."

MORE NOISE PLE...
NATURAL BORN KILLERS
I AM...
...CRETLY AN AN... BOR
PRISON
NATURAL BORN KILLERS soundtrack
MORE NOISE PLEASE

TODAY, STEVEN JESSE BERNSTEIN'S WORK IS HIGHLY REGARDED. AS HIS MENTOR **WILLIAM S. BURROUGHS** SAID:

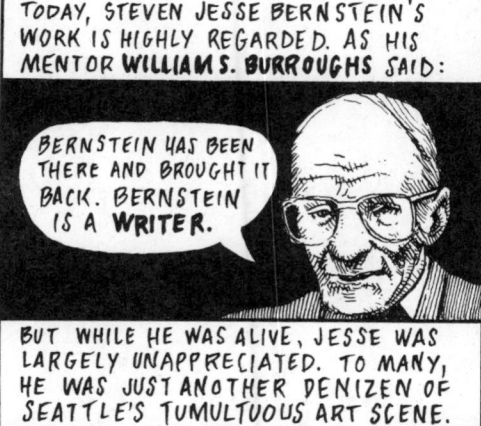

BERNSTEIN HAS BEEN THERE AND BROUGHT IT BACK. BERNSTEIN IS A **WRITER**.

BUT WHILE HE WAS ALIVE, JESSE WAS LARGELY UNAPPRECIATED. TO MANY, HE WAS JUST ANOTHER DENIZEN OF SEATTLE'S TUMULTUOUS ART SCENE.

IN MID-1991, ONE OF THE SEATTLE MAGAZINES I WROTE FOR ASSIGNED ME A STORY ABOUT A GROUP OF PEOPLE WHO WERE OPERATING AN UNDERGROUND CB NETWORK.

They live in old schoolbuses parked alongside the railroad tracks south of the Kingdome.

I'LL ALWAYS REMEMBER MY LAST ENCOUNTER WITH SEATTLE'S FOREMOST POET. HERE'S WHAT LED UP TO IT.

I'll check it out.

THEY WERE A DEDICATED BUNCH OF GOOD SAMARITANS, LED BY A CHARISMATIC FELLOW WITH LOTS OF ENERGY.

My handle's 'Wino.'

Copy that, Barnacle Bill. Georgia Peach will stop by in about five minutes with a first-aid kit.

Copy. May God bless you with a heavenly ten-four!

THIS SIDE UP

WINO AND HIS FRIENDS PROVIDED CAMARADERIE AND ASSISTANCE FOR THE LONG-DISTANCE TRUCKERS THAT TRAVELLED THE REGION'S HIGHWAYS.

Why are you doing this?

It's the best thing I could possibly do with my life.

We make a huge difference.

I SPENT HOURS WITH THEM TAKING NOTES.

THE NEXT DAY, ON MY WAY TO WORK, I WAS THINKING ABOUT THE STORY.

What if I lead off with-- say, that looks like Wino!

Hey Wino, is that you?

No, hehheh-- but I know who Wino is.

Jesse Bernstein! Sorry man, but you look a lot like Wino, and he was on my mind.

I've been mistaken for him before. It's cool.

HONK!

HUVA!
MOVE IT YOU MORONS!

Gotta go-- I'm busy.

Yeah, me too.

BEEP. HONK

Fuck you, ASSHOLE!

Fuck you!

HONK!

THAT WAS THE LAST I SAW OF JESSE BERNSTEIN.

32